Mathematics for Christian Living Series

D1481101

Gaining Skill With Arithmetic

Grade 5

Tests

Rod and Staff Publishers, Inc.

Hwy. 172, Crockett, Kentucky 41413

Telephone: (606) 522-4348

ISBN 978-07399-0473-2

Catalog no. 13511.3

13   14   15   —   20   19   18   17   16   15

12. Chapter 1 Test

Score _____

Name _____   Date _____

A. *Write the answers.* (1 pt. each; 50 total)

1.

8	6	9	10	12	7	11	14	8
+9	+7	+6	-7	-5	+9	-6	-8	+7

2.

7	9	8	6	4	9	7	6	8
×9	×6	×8	×7	×8	×9	×8	×8	×9

3. 7)‾49‾   4)‾36‾   5)‾45‾   7)‾28‾   9)‾54‾   6)‾18‾

4. Match by writing the correct letters in the blanks. Some letters will be used more than once.

```
    16  ____              329  ____
  × 27  ____              978  ____
   112  ____            + 325  ____
    32  ____            1,632  ____
   432  ____
                         503  ____
         59 ____        - 289  ____
   ____ 7)413 ____        214  ____
```

a. addend   g. multiplicand
b. difference   h. subtrahend
c. dividend   i. sum
d. divisor   j. product
e. minuend   k. quotient
f. multiplier   l. partial product

5. Write numerals for these number words.

a. _____ twelve thousand, five

b. _____ fifty-five million, two hundred twenty thousand

c. _____ 4 million, 40 thousand, 400

d. _____ 728 million, 176 thousand, 95

6. Change these to Roman numerals.

17 _____   59 _____   100 _____   94 _____

7. What times do these clocks show? **a.** _____  **b.** _____

8. Is the school day over at 3:00 A.M.
or 3:00 P.M.? _____

B. *Follow the signs, and work carefully.* *(2 pt. each; 50 total)*

9.

7	9		65		764		
6	8	38	84	538	389	5,940	4,387
5	8	72	51	217	457	1,255	7,456
+ 9	+ 5	+ 99	+ 48	+ 782	+ 241	+ 2,587	+ 3,646

10.

600	943	812	8,019	5,724	7,302
− 275	− 336	− 728	− 3,427	− 1,362	− 5,899

11.

37	159	742	675	4,256	6,893
× 5	× 6	× 9	× 4	× 8	× 3

12.   5)19   3)264   7)126   4)530   6)96

C. *Write add, subtract, multiply, or divide.*   *(1 pt. each; 5 total)*

13. _____ **a.** Kevin weighed two boxes. How much more did the one box weigh?

_____ **b.** If pencils cost 7¢ each, how many can be bought for $1.40?

_____ **c.** Erasers cost 12¢ each. What is the cost of 24 erasers?

_____ **d.** Mother had $50.00. She spent some. How much money did she have left?

_____ **e.** Marcia baked two kinds of cookies. How many cookies did she bake in all?

D. *Solve these reading problems.* *(2 pt. each; total 4)*

14. Sister Miriam bought 8 notebooks at 64¢ each. How much did she pay for the notebooks?

_____

15. Father bought gasoline for $14.75 and oil for $1.39. What was his change from $20.00?

_____

Subtract points wrong from 100% for score.

21. Chapter 2 Test

Score _____

Name _____   Date _____

A. *Write the answers only.* (1 pt. each; 15 total)

1.

8	12	11	12	12	12	11	12	10
× 9	× 8	× 11	× 12	× 9	× 11	× 10	× 7	× 10

2.   9)81   11)110   12)60   10)90   11)66   7)63

B. *Follow the directions.* (1 pt. each; 18 total)

3. Change to Roman numerals.

1,000 _____   118 _____   654 _____   979 _____

4. Change to Arabic numerals.

D _____   MCCC _____   CDXXV _____   CCXLVII _____

5. Place commas where they are needed. Circle the digit in hundred millions' place.

90847362170

6. Write numerals for these number words.

a. three billion _____

b. twenty-five billion, six hundred million _____

c. 816 billion, 75 million, 6 thousand, 450 _____

7. Write < or > between each pair of numbers.

599,999 _____ 601,999   72,300,010 _____ 72,058,969

8. Round to the nearest thousand: 653,824 _____

9. Round to the nearest ten thousand: 653,824 _____

10. Round to the nearest hundred thousand: 653,824 _____

C. *Do these exercises.* (2 pt. each; 12 total)

11. Tell what pieces of money should be given as change.
Amount of purchase—$6.68; amount given—$20.00

_____

12.

$40.00	$15.00	4,293	9,318	5,670
− 13.55	− 12.78	× 5	× 6	× 7

D. *Multiply. Check by exchanging factors.* *(2 pt. each problem and each check; 12 total)*

13.
$$\begin{array}{r} 72 \\ \times\, 96 \\ \hline \end{array}$$
$$\begin{array}{r} 89 \\ \times\, 14 \\ \hline \end{array}$$
$$\begin{array}{r} 60 \\ \times\, 68 \\ \hline \end{array}$$

E. *Divide. Check by multiplication.* *(2 pt. each problem and each check; 24 total)*

14. $4\overline{)29}$ $5\overline{)380}$ $6\overline{)920}$

15. $7\overline{)2,530}$ $3\overline{)4,638}$ $4\overline{)5,000}$

F. *Solve these reading problems.* *(4 pt. each; 20 total)*

16. The Bible tells us that Adam lived 930 years and his son Seth lived 912 years. How many more years did Adam live than Seth?

_____

17. Sister Edna bought three packs of flower seeds for $0.49 each and potting soil for $5.95. What was her total bill?

_____

18. Nelson spent $13.89 on a tank of gasoline. What was his change from $20.00?

_____

19. Every spring the Moyers raise green onions to sell. They tie the onions in bunches with six in a bunch. One week they had 325 bunches. How many onions were in the bunches altogether?

_____

20. The Moyers also raise radishes. They put 8 radishes in a bunch. How many bunches of radishes can they make with 680 radishes?

_____

Subtract points wrong from 100% for score.

31. Chapter 3 Test

Score _____

Name _____ Date _____

A. Do these exercises. *(1 pt. each; 34 total)*

1. Write **P** for proper fraction, **I** for improper fraction, or **M** for mixed number.

$3\frac{1}{2}$ ____ $\frac{3}{4}$ ____ $\frac{4}{3}$ ____ $\frac{10}{10}$ ____ $\frac{10}{15}$ ____ $5\frac{1}{10}$ ____

2. Label the denominator and the numerator of this fraction: $\frac{2}{3}$ _____

_____

3. Another name for "numerator and denominator of a fraction" is _____ of a fraction.

4. Put **X** before the pair of like fractions.

_____ $\frac{2}{3}$ $\frac{2}{5}$ _____ $\frac{1}{4}$ $\frac{3}{4}$ _____ $\frac{3}{5}$ $\frac{5}{3}$

5. Count by fourths to fill in the missing numbers.

$\frac{1}{4}$, _____, _____, 1, _____, $1\frac{1}{2}$, _____, _____, $2\frac{1}{4}$, _____, $2\frac{3}{4}$, _____

6. Fill in the missing numbers to make equivalent fractions.

$\frac{1}{3} = \frac{}{9}$ $\frac{2}{3} = \frac{8}{}$ $\frac{3}{4} = \frac{6}{}$ $\frac{1}{8} = \frac{3}{}$ $\frac{5}{8} = \frac{}{16}$

7. Reduce these fractions to lowest terms.

$\frac{6}{10}$ $\frac{10}{20}$ $\frac{4}{16}$ $\frac{5}{15}$ $\frac{8}{20}$ $\frac{12}{18}$

8. Change these improper fractions to whole or mixed numbers. Do your work on other paper if you cannot do it in your head.

$\frac{8}{3}$ $\frac{8}{2}$ $\frac{5}{2}$ $\frac{6}{6}$ $\frac{14}{4}$ $\frac{10}{8}$

B. Write the answers only. *(1 pt. each; 15 total)*

9. $\frac{1}{7}$ of 42 = _____ $\frac{1}{9}$ of 36 = _____ $\frac{1}{5}$ of 30 = _____

10. $\frac{3}{7}$ of 42 = _____ $\frac{5}{9}$ of 36 = _____ $\frac{4}{5}$ of 30 = _____

11. $\frac{2}{3}$ of 24 = _____ $\frac{3}{4}$ of 12 = _____ $\frac{5}{8}$ of 40 = _____

12. $1\frac{1}{2} \times 14$ = _____ $2\frac{1}{3} \times 6$ = _____ $3\frac{1}{4} \times 8$ = _____

13. Write as fractions.

4 divided by 7 _____ $1 \div 5$ _____ $\frac{1}{4}$ of 3 _____

C. *Follow the signs. Express remainders in division as fractions. Reduce all fraction answers to lowest terms.* (2 pt. each; 36 total)

14.
$$\begin{array}{r} 780 \\ \times\ 37 \\ \hline \end{array} \qquad \begin{array}{r} 356 \\ \times\ 49 \\ \hline \end{array} \qquad \begin{array}{r} 924 \\ \times\ 78 \\ \hline \end{array} \qquad 4\overline{)386} \qquad 6\overline{)754} \qquad 5\overline{)4,233}$$

15.
$$\begin{array}{r} \frac{7}{8} \\ +\ \frac{1}{8} \\ \hline \end{array} \qquad \begin{array}{r} \frac{3}{4} \\ +\ \frac{3}{4} \\ \hline \end{array} \qquad \begin{array}{r} \frac{5}{10} \\ +\ \frac{3}{10} \\ \hline \end{array} \qquad \begin{array}{r} \frac{9}{16} \\ +\ \frac{3}{16} \\ \hline \end{array} \qquad \begin{array}{r} \frac{7}{9} \\ +\ \frac{5}{9} \\ \hline \end{array} \qquad \begin{array}{r} \frac{2}{3} \\ +\ \frac{2}{3} \\ \hline \end{array}$$

16.
$$\begin{array}{r} 3\frac{1}{8} \\ +\ 1\frac{3}{8} \\ \hline \end{array} \qquad \begin{array}{r} 5\frac{7}{12} \\ +\ 3\frac{1}{12} \\ \hline \end{array} \qquad \begin{array}{r} \frac{11}{16} \\ -\ \frac{7}{16} \\ \hline \end{array} \qquad \begin{array}{r} \frac{5}{6} \\ -\ \frac{1}{6} \\ \hline \end{array} \qquad \begin{array}{r} 6\frac{7}{8} \\ -\ 2\frac{1}{8} \\ \hline \end{array} \qquad \begin{array}{r} 9\frac{7}{10} \\ -\ 3\frac{3}{10} \\ \hline \end{array}$$

D. *Solve these reading problems.* (3 pt. each; 12 total)

17. Marie brushes her teeth three times a day. How many times does she brush her teeth in a year (365 days)?

_____

18. Matthew, Michael, and Thomas are sharing 8 cookies that Mother gave them. How many cookies can each boy have?

_____

19. Carolyn learned 45 Bible verses in 6 weeks. At that rate she learned _____ verses each week.

20. John Wycliffe, the first man to translate the Bible into English, began his translation about 1379. The King James version of the English Bible was completed in 1611, which was _____ years later.

41. Chapter 4 Test (First Quarter)

Score _____

Name _____ Date _____

A. *Write the key numbers for these measures.* (1 pt. each; 15 total)

1. 1 yard = _____ feet   1 foot = _____ inches   1 pound = _____ ounces
2. 1 day = _____ hours   1 yard = _____ inches   1 hour = _____ minutes
3. 1 pint = _____ cups   1 quart = _____ pints   1 bushel = _____ pecks
4. 1 quart = _____ cups   1 peck = _____ quarts   1 decade = _____ years
5. 1 year = _____ days   1 mile = _____ feet   1 century = _____ years

B. *Multiply or divide to change these units of measure.* (1 pt. each; 12 total)

6. 6 ft. = _____ in.   6 qt. = _____ gal.   6 ft. = _____ yd.
7. 8 qt. = _____ pt.   10 pk. = _____ bu.   3 tons = _____ lb.
8. 7 cups = _____ pt.   48 mo. = _____ yr.   2 days = _____ wk.
9. 4 bu. = _____ pk.   3 decades = _____ yr.   8 oz. = _____ lb.

C. *Write the answers only.* (1 pt. each; 9 total)

10. $\frac{3}{5}$ of 15 = _____ $\frac{2}{3}$ of 36 = _____ $\frac{7}{8}$ of 24 = _____
11. $1\frac{1}{3} \times 18$ = _____ $2\frac{1}{4} \times 8$ = _____ $1\frac{1}{8} \times 40$ = _____
12. $3 \div 8$ = _____ $1 \div 2$ = _____ $\frac{1}{5}$ of 4 = _____

D. *Follow the directions.* (1 pt. each; 20 total)

13. Measure the line after each letter and write its length in the blank.

    _____ a. ——————————————————————————————

    _____ b. ————————————————————————————

14. Write the lengths to which the arrows point.

    a. _____   b. _____   c. _____   d. _____   e. _____   f. _____

    a. ↓   b. ↓   c. ↓   d. ↓   e. ↓   f. ↓

    | 1 | 2 | 3 | 4 | 5 | 6 |

15. Reduce to lowest terms. $\frac{5}{15}$ _____ $\frac{8}{12}$ _____ $\frac{16}{20}$ _____

16. Change to mixed numbers in simplest form. $\frac{11}{3}$ _____ $\frac{9}{6}$ _____ $\frac{14}{8}$ _____

17. Write with Roman numerals: **a.** 586 _____   **b.** 1,954 _____

18. Write 28 billion, 650 million as a numeral.   _____

19. Round 465,397 to the nearest ten thousand.   _____

20. Count the money. _____

21. Write the time. _____

E. *Follow the signs.* (2 pt. each; 30 total)

22.

```
    5 quarts  3 cups          6 years   4 months        9 hours  16 minutes
  + 4 quarts  2 cups        - 2 years  10 months       - 4 hours  35 minutes
```

23.

```
    8,021       7,839        4,750      $50.00          4 7/16          7/8
  - 2,385      ×    6        ×   9     - 27.49        - 1 5/16        + 5/8
```

24.

```
                             749
  5)875      6)3,844         672       56,784
                             367       74,836            59            358
                           + 485     + 83,967          × 38          × 74
```

F. *Solve these reading problems.* (3 pt. each; 12 total)

25. When Ann's mother makes pudding, she uses a recipe that calls for 8 cups of milk. How many quarts of milk is that?

_____

26. Galen Miller and his two sons are baling hay. The first wagon load had 167 bales on it. If the Millers get six loads that size, how many bales of hay will they have altogether?

_____

27. One year the weather was very dry. When the Millers baled a 4-acre field of hay, they got only 36 bales. How many bales of hay did they get per acre?

_____

28. Sister Joan is studying Spanish. She bought a Spanish–English dictionary for $5.79 and a Spanish New Testament for $3.75. What was her change from $20.00?

_____

Subtract points wrong from 100% for score.

50. Chapter 5 Test

Score _____

Name _____   Date _____

A. *Write the answers only.* (1 pt. each; 44 total)

1.
$$\begin{array}{r} 10 \\ \times\,3 \\ \hline \end{array} \quad \begin{array}{r} 11 \\ \times\,7 \\ \hline \end{array} \quad \begin{array}{r} 12 \\ \times\,8 \\ \hline \end{array} \quad \begin{array}{r} 12 \\ \times\,5 \\ \hline \end{array} \quad \begin{array}{r} 10 \\ \times\,5 \\ \hline \end{array} \quad \begin{array}{r} 11 \\ \times\,2 \\ \hline \end{array} \quad \begin{array}{r} 12 \\ \times\,3 \\ \hline \end{array} \quad \begin{array}{r} 12 \\ \times\,6 \\ \hline \end{array} \quad \begin{array}{r} 12 \\ \times\,4 \\ \hline \end{array}$$

2.
$$\begin{array}{r} 10 \\ \times\,8 \\ \hline \end{array} \quad \begin{array}{r} 12 \\ \times\,10 \\ \hline \end{array} \quad \begin{array}{r} 11 \\ \times\,12 \\ \hline \end{array} \quad \begin{array}{r} 10 \\ \times\,10 \\ \hline \end{array} \quad \begin{array}{r} 12 \\ \times\,9 \\ \hline \end{array} \quad \begin{array}{r} 11 \\ \times\,11 \\ \hline \end{array} \quad \begin{array}{r} 12 \\ \times\,12 \\ \hline \end{array} \quad \begin{array}{r} 12 \\ \times\,7 \\ \hline \end{array} \quad \begin{array}{r} 11 \\ \times\,10 \\ \hline \end{array}$$

3. $10\overline{)60}$ $12\overline{)60}$ $11\overline{)44}$ $10\overline{)100}$ $12\overline{)108}$ $11\overline{)132}$

4. $12\overline{)24}$ $11\overline{)99}$ $12\overline{)84}$ $12\overline{)120}$ $11\overline{)121}$ $10\overline{)110}$

5. $12\overline{)72}$ $11\overline{)11}$ $10\overline{)90}$ $10\overline{)120}$ $12\overline{)144}$ $12\overline{)132}$

6. $4 \times 14 =$ _____ $6 \times 71 =$ _____ $3 \times 83 =$ _____ $5 \times 16 =$ _____

7. $2 \times 95 =$ _____ $8 \times 22 =$ _____ $4 \times 25 =$ _____ $7 \times 33 =$ _____

B. *Do these exercises.* (1 pt. each blank; 13 total)

8. Round to the nearest ten.

37 _____   14 _____   52 _____   721 _____   849 _____   3,743 _____

9. Write each price in two ways.

   a. thirteen cents _____ _____   b. seven dollars _____ _____

10. Write the value of these bills.

   a. _____   b. _____   c. _____

C. *Copy numbers 11–13 in straight columns at the right, and solve.* (*2 pt. each; 6 total*)

11. $56.78 + $15 + $3.14 + $0.06

12. $31 – $26.02

13. $18.97 – $5.79

D. *Solve these problems.* (*2 pt. each; 30 total*)

14.

$$\begin{array}{r} \$0.75 \\ \times\ 34 \\ \hline \end{array} \qquad \begin{array}{r} \$2.19 \\ \times\ \ 7 \\ \hline \end{array} \qquad \begin{array}{r} \$4.63 \\ \times\ 26 \\ \hline \end{array} \qquad 6\overline{)\$1.68} \qquad 5\overline{)\$0.45}$$

15. $30\overline{)840} \qquad 22\overline{)176} \qquad 13\overline{)713} \qquad 50\overline{)400} \qquad 14\overline{)350}$

16. $12\overline{)690} \qquad 40\overline{)180} \qquad 23\overline{)161} \qquad 32\overline{)480} \qquad 11\overline{)792}$

E. *Circle the best estimate for each problem. Then find the exact answer.*
(*1 pt. each estimate, 2 pt. each answer; 12 total*)

17.   Aunt Ruth bought 12 pounds of apples at $0.59 a pound.
What was her bill?

$0.70 $5.00 $7.00 $12.00   _____

18.   Father bought a new telephone for $37.89. What was his
change from a 50-dollar bill?

$3 $12 $46 $88   _____

19.   A set of 6 dinner plates sells for $13.44. What is the cost of
one plate?

a little less than $2.00   about $50.00
a little more than $2.00   about $70.00   _____

20.   What is the total cost of 2 cans of soup for 41¢ each, a box
of crackers for $1.69, and a jar of peanut butter for $3.27?

$5.40 $5.80 $7.00 $85.00   _____

Subtract points wrong from 100% for score.

60. Chapter 6 Test

Score _____

Name _____ Date _____

A. *Write the answers in the blanks.* *(1 pt. each; 32 total)*

1. _____ × 5 = 15   8 × _____ = 72   12 × 7 = _____   _____ × 6 = 42

2. 9 × _____ = 63   _____ × 3 = 27   _____ × 4 = 8   7 × 8 = _____

3. 6 ÷ _____ = 2   _____ ÷ 6 = 2   48 ÷ _____ = 6   _____ ÷ 6 = 4

4. 45 ÷ 5 = _____   36 ÷ _____ = 9   _____ ÷ 3 = 6   64 ÷ _____ = 8

5. 3 × 18 = _____   6 × 25 = _____   4 × 37 = _____   7 × 36 = _____

6. 10 × 591 = _____   10 × 70 = _____   100 × 14 = _____   100 × 20 = _____

7. 12 + 16 = _____   14 + 30 = _____   26 + 8 = _____   15 + 17 = _____

8. 43 − 10 = _____   28 − 6 = _____   55 − 13 = _____   34 − 7 = _____

B. *Round these numbers.* *(1 pt. each; 11 total)*

9. Round to the nearest ten.

   59 _____   384 _____   1,746 _____   6,235 _____

10. Round to the nearest hundred.

   384 _____   1,746 _____   6,235 _____   32,681 _____

11. Round to the nearest thousand.

   6,235 _____   32,681 _____   490,928 _____

C. *Do these exercises.* *(3 pt. each; 39 total)*

12. Follow the signs. Check by going over your work.

$$
\begin{array}{r} 70{,}002 \\ -\ 28{,}916 \\ \hline \end{array}
\qquad
\begin{array}{r} 38{,}410 \\ -\ 16{,}905 \\ \hline \end{array}
\qquad
\begin{array}{r} 846 \\ \times\ 700 \\ \hline \end{array}
\qquad
\begin{array}{r} 360 \\ \times\ 800 \\ \hline \end{array}
\qquad
\begin{array}{r} 583 \\ \times\ 350 \\ \hline \end{array}
$$

13. Multiply. Check by exchanging factors.

$$
\begin{array}{r} 743 \\ \times\,172 \\ \hline \end{array}
\qquad
\begin{array}{r} 219 \\ \times\,580 \\ \hline \end{array}
\qquad
\begin{array}{r} 860 \\ \times\,623 \\ \hline \end{array}
\qquad
\begin{array}{r} 157 \\ \times\,642 \\ \hline \end{array}
$$

14. Divide. Check by multiplying.

$$
21\overline{)546} \qquad 13\overline{)325} \qquad 32\overline{)256} \qquad 14\overline{)327}
$$

D. *Write A, S, M, or D to tell which operation should be used to find each answer. Then solve the problems.* (1 pt. each letter, 2 pt. each answer; 12 total)

15. Motto hangers come in packages of 8. Mother bought 4 packages of motto hangers. How many hangers did Mother buy? _____

_____

16. Jerome collected 60 different kinds of leaves, and Thelma collected 50 different kinds. How many leaves do Jerome and Thelma have together? _____

_____

17. Jerome has _____ more kinds of leaves than Thelma. _____

18. If 84 people were separated into 7 groups, how many people would be in each group? _____

_____

E. *These problems require two steps. Solve them carefully.* (4 pt. each; 8 total)

19. One dozen 4-page tracts cost $0.60, and one dozen 8-page tracts cost $0.65. What is the total cost of 15 dozen 4-page tracts and 1 dozen 8-page tracts?

_____

20. What is the cost of $1\frac{1}{4}$ pounds of cheese at $2.16 a pound?

_____

Subtract points wrong from 100% for score.

70. Chapter 7 Test

Score _____

Name _____ Date _____

A. *Follow the directions.* *(4 pt. for number 1; 1 pt. each blank; 22 total)*

1. Circle the prime numbers: 3   7   9   13   15   22   29

2. List the factor pairs for these numbers.

6 _____   14 _____   16 _____   30 _____

_____   _____   _____   _____

_____   _____

_____

3. List the factors of these numbers in order.

a. 6 _____   c. 16 _____

b. 14 _____   d. 30 _____

4. Write the greatest common factor of each pair.

6 and 14 _____   6 and 30 _____   16 and 36 _____

B. *Do these exercises.* *(6–8: 2 pt. each; 5 and 9–11: 1 pt. each; 19 total)*

5. Finish the factor trees for these numbers.

a. (10)   b. (12)   c. (20)   d. (36)

6. Write 12 multiples of 5. _____

7. Write 12 multiples of 6. _____

8. Write 12 multiples of 10. _____

9. Write the lowest common multiple of each pair.

5 and 6 _____   5 and 10 _____   6 and 10 _____

10. Reduce these fractions to lowest terms, using the largest common factors.

$\frac{12}{30}$ $\frac{16}{24}$ $\frac{9}{36}$ $\frac{9}{15}$ $\frac{18}{22}$

11. Write the smallest common denominator for $\frac{1}{2}$ and $\frac{1}{3}$. _____

C. *Change each pair of fractions to like fractions.* (2 pt. each; 16 total)

12. $\frac{7}{8}$ $\frac{3}{4}$ _____ $\frac{1}{2}$ $\frac{7}{12}$ _____ $\frac{2}{3}$ $\frac{1}{4}$ _____ $\frac{3}{5}$ $\frac{1}{2}$ _____

13. $\frac{1}{2}$ $\frac{2}{3}$ _____ $\frac{1}{2}$ $\frac{9}{16}$ _____ $\frac{1}{4}$ $\frac{1}{6}$ _____ $\frac{2}{3}$ $\frac{5}{8}$ _____

D. *Write $<$ or $>$ between each pair of fractions.* (2 pt. each; 8 total)

14. $\frac{3}{4}$ ____ $\frac{5}{6}$ $\frac{1}{2}$ ____ $\frac{7}{16}$ $\frac{1}{3}$ ____ $\frac{3}{8}$ $\frac{1}{2}$ ____ $\frac{2}{5}$

E. *Find the average of each set of numbers.* (3 pt. each; 9 total)

15. 6, 9, 7, 9, 6, 6, 6 _____

16. $2.40, $3.00, $2.50, $1.70 _____

17. 45, 24, 56, 42, 60, 43 _____

F. *Solve these reading problems.* (4 pt. each; 24 total)

18. Alvin and Mabel timed each other to see how many multiplication facts they could say in a minute. Alvin said 26 facts the first minute. How many facts could he say in 3 minutes at that rate?

_____

19. Mabel said 32 facts the first minute. At that rate she could say _____ facts in 4 minutes.

20. The early morning temperatures one week were 18°, 26°, 16°, 21°, and 24°. What was the average morning temperature?

_____

21. A 6-acre field of corn yielded 690 bushels of corn. What was the average number of bushels per acre?

_____

22. The cooks at a Bible school need 216 hot dog buns. If 12 buns come in a pack, how many packs of buns are needed?

_____

23. Early in the season, string beans cost $2.95 a half peck. When beans were more plentiful, they cost $11.75 a bushel. How much did a family save on a bushel of beans if they waited until the price went down? (Hint: There are 8 half pecks in a bushel.)

_____

81. Chapter 8 Test (Midyear)

Score _____

Name _____ Date _____

A. *Fill in the blanks.* (1–2 and 7–8: 1/2 pt. each; 3–6 and 9–10: 1 pt. each; 29 total)

1. $12 \times 11 =$ _____ $48 \div 8 =$ _____ $9 \times 7 =$ _____ $54 \div 6 =$ _____

2. $40 \div$ _____ $= 5$ _____ $\times 7 = 42$ _____ $\div 2 = 8$ $12 \times$ _____ $= 84$

3. $28 + 10 =$ _____ $12 + 19 =$ _____ $25 + 32 =$ _____ $36 + 17 =$ _____

4. $19 - 6 =$ _____ $35 - 20 =$ _____ $21 - 7 =$ _____ $33 - 8 =$ _____

5. $100 \times 75 =$ _____ $10 \times 60 =$ _____ $7 \times 40 =$ _____ $6 \times 26 =$ _____

6. $\frac{1}{4}$ of $32 =$ _____ $\frac{3}{5}$ of $45 =$ _____ $2 \div 3 =$ _____ $1\frac{1}{2} \times 14 =$ _____

7. 1 yd. = _____ in.   1 mi. = _____ ft.   1 ton = _____ lb.

8. 1 bu. = _____ pk.   1 qt. = _____ pt.   1 yr. = _____ days

9. 3 gal. = _____ qt.   24 ft. = _____ yd.   4 cups = _____ pt.

10. 4 days = _____ hr.   30 min. = _____ hr.   18 in. = _____ ft.

B. *Follow the directions.* (4 pt. for number 11; 1 pt. each blank; 25 total)

11. Circle all the numbers by which 4,512 can be divided evenly.

    2   3   4   5   6   9   10

12. List in order all the factors of 20. _____

13. Write the value of the 5 in 165,390,286,749. _____

14. Reduce to lowest terms: $\frac{14}{24}$ _____ $\frac{18}{30}$ _____ $\frac{9}{36}$ _____

15. Write < or > between the fractions: $\frac{1}{2}$ _____ $\frac{2}{3}$ $\frac{3}{8}$ _____ $\frac{9}{16}$

16. Change to whole or mixed numbers: $\frac{14}{4}$ _____ $\frac{6}{2}$ _____ $\frac{8}{5}$ _____

17. Change to simplest form: $4\frac{5}{5}$ _____ $3\frac{16}{12}$ _____ $1\frac{5}{3}$ _____

18. Change to improper fractions: $5 = \frac{}{2}$ $3\frac{1}{2} = \frac{}{2}$ $1\frac{7}{8} = \frac{}{8}$

19. Write the lowest common denominators: $\frac{3}{4}$ $\frac{1}{3}$ _____ $\frac{1}{2}$ $\frac{4}{5}$ _____ $\frac{7}{8}$ $\frac{1}{2}$ _____

20. Write the lengths to which the arrows point.

    a. _____   b. _____

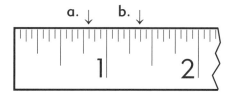

C. *Follow the signs, and work carefully.* (2 pt. each; 40 total)

21.

$$
\begin{array}{r}
8 \\
7 \\
6 \\
9 \\
+\ 6 \\
\end{array}
\qquad
\begin{array}{r}
597 \\
348 \\
871 \\
+\ 627 \\
\end{array}
\qquad
\begin{array}{r}
48{,}762 \\
27{,}563 \\
+\ 75{,}289 \\
\end{array}
\qquad
\begin{array}{r}
8{,}020 \\
-\ 2{,}824 \\
\end{array}
\qquad
\begin{array}{r}
64{,}107 \\
-\ 53{,}483 \\
\end{array}
$$

22.

$$
\begin{array}{r}
9{,}340 \\
\times\quad 8 \\
\end{array}
\qquad
\begin{array}{r}
529 \\
\times\ 64 \\
\end{array}
\qquad
\begin{array}{r}
673 \\
\times\ 457 \\
\end{array}
\qquad
24\overline{)168}
\qquad
13\overline{)585}
$$

23.

$$
\begin{array}{r}
\frac{7}{8} \\
+\ \frac{9}{16} \\
\end{array}
\qquad
\begin{array}{r}
\frac{5}{12} \\
+\ \frac{3}{4} \\
\end{array}
\qquad
\begin{array}{r}
2\frac{5}{9} \\
+\ 3\frac{1}{9} \\
\end{array}
\qquad
\begin{array}{r}
3\frac{5}{8} \\
+\ \frac{7}{8} \\
\end{array}
\qquad
\begin{array}{r}
4\frac{2}{3} \\
+\ 2\frac{1}{2} \\
\end{array}
$$

24.

$$
\begin{array}{r}
\frac{11}{12} \\
-\ \frac{1}{3} \\
\end{array}
\qquad
\begin{array}{r}
\frac{5}{6} \\
-\ \frac{1}{2} \\
\end{array}
\qquad
\begin{array}{r}
4\frac{3}{10} \\
-\ 1\frac{7}{10} \\
\end{array}
\qquad
\begin{array}{r}
2 \\
-\ \frac{3}{5} \\
\end{array}
\qquad
\begin{array}{r}
5\frac{3}{8} \\
-\ 3\frac{3}{4} \\
\end{array}
$$

D. *Solve these reading problems.* (2 pt. each; 6 total)

25. Mother used $8\frac{1}{2}$ cups of white flour and $5\frac{1}{2}$ cups of whole wheat flour to make a batch of bread. What was the total amount of flour that she used?

_____

26. Attendance at Bible school was as follows: 147 people on the first night, 162 people on the second night, 158 people on the third night, and 149 people on the fourth night. What was the average attendance on these nights?

_____

27. Mother used 3 cups of sugar to sweeten a large bowlful of applesauce. She thought the applesauce was too sweet, so she used $\frac{3}{4}$ cup less sugar in the next bowlful. How much sugar did Mother use the second time?

_____

Subtract points wrong from 100% for score.

90. Chapter 9 Test

Score _____

Name _____ Date _____

A. *Fill in the blanks.* *(1 pt. each blank; 24 total)*

1. $6 \times 7 + 5 =$ _____ $3 \times 0 + 6 =$ _____ $5 \times 7 + 6 =$ _____
2. $8 \times 9 + 4 =$ _____ $6 \times 8 + 5 =$ _____ $0 \times 5 + 4 =$ _____
3. $8 \times 17 =$ _____ $3 \times 94 =$ _____ $5 \times 65 =$ _____
4. $7 \times 29 =$ _____ $4 \times 75 =$ _____ $6 \times 16 =$ _____

5. 9 qt. = _____ gal. _____ qt.   13 days = _____ wk. _____ days
6. 11 ft. = _____ yd. _____ ft.   8 pt. = _____ qt. _____ pt.
7. 29 mo. = _____ yr. _____ mo.   18 qt. = _____ pk. _____ qt.

B. *Do the following exercises.* *(1 pt. each; 11 total)*

8. Round to the nearest ten: 67 _____   854 _____   3,628 _____

9. Round to the nearest hundred: 854 _____   3,628 _____

10. Write how many digits will be in each quotient. Do not solve the problems.

$7\overline{)893}$ $13\overline{)890}$ $52\overline{)436}$ $47\overline{)6,210}$ $25\overline{)2,255}$ $38\overline{)41,820}$

C. *Follow the directions.* *(2 pt. each problem, 2 pt. each written check; 50 total)*

11. Multiply these measures.

    7 bushels 3 pecks   4 feet 4 inches   3 pints 1 cup
             × 4   × 5   × 5

12. Multiply. Check by exchanging factors.

$$\begin{array}{r} 608 \\ \times 453 \\ \hline \end{array} \qquad \begin{array}{r} 319 \\ \times 604 \\ \hline \end{array} \qquad \begin{array}{r} 580 \\ \times 265 \\ \hline \end{array}$$

13. Multiply. Check by going over your work.

$$\begin{array}{r} 230 \\ \times 970 \\ \hline \end{array} \quad \begin{array}{r} 800 \\ \times 278 \\ \hline \end{array} \quad \begin{array}{r} 902 \\ \times 580 \\ \hline \end{array} \quad \begin{array}{r} 709 \\ \times 907 \\ \hline \end{array} \quad \begin{array}{r} 396 \\ \times 600 \\ \hline \end{array}$$

14. Divide. Check by multiplying.

$16\overline{)688}$ $38\overline{)8,753}$ $44\overline{)2,508}$

15. Divide. Check by going over your work.

$59\overline{)2,006}$ $27\overline{)5,547}$ $18\overline{)7,214}$ $43\overline{)68,886}$ $35\overline{)17,780}$

D. *Solve these reading problems.* *(3 pt. each; 12 total)*

16. At Root's Potato Chips, twelve 7-ounce bags of chips are put into each cardboard box. How many full boxes can be made with 450 bags of chips?

_____

17. The Grants have invited several families from church to come for Sunday dinner. Mother plans to make applesauce jello. For a large recipe she needs 10 cups of applesauce. How many quart jars of applesauce does she need to open?

_____

18. In November Mr. Jackson had 86 sheep in his pens. By spring 12 sheep had been sold, 5 sheep had died, and there were 57 new lambs. How many sheep did Mr. Jackson have then?

_____

19. Neighbor Dan sells corn for $3.25 a bushel and wheat for $3.50 a bushel. One week he sold 64 bushels of corn and half that many bushels of wheat. How much did Dan receive altogether for the corn and wheat?

_____

Subtract points wrong from 100% for score.

100. Chapter 10 Test

Score _____

Name _____ Date _____

A. *Follow the directions.* *(1 pt. each blank; 2 pt. each problem in row 2; 28 total)*

1. Write the lowest common denominator for adding each set of fractions.

    a. $\frac{1}{2}$ $\frac{2}{3}$ $\frac{1}{4}$ _____   **b.** $\frac{5}{8}$ $\frac{1}{3}$ $\frac{3}{4}$ _____   **c.** $\frac{9}{10}$ $\frac{1}{2}$ $\frac{3}{5}$ _____

2. Add or subtract.

$$
\begin{array}{ccccc}
\frac{5}{6} & \frac{1}{2} & \frac{7}{10} & 3\frac{7}{12} & 5\frac{1}{9} \\
\frac{1}{3} & \frac{5}{8} & \frac{4}{5} & +4\frac{3}{4} & -3\frac{2}{3} \\
+\frac{1}{2} & +\frac{3}{16} & +\frac{2}{3} & &
\end{array}
$$

3. Write in two ways: as decimals and as common fractions or mixed numbers.

    a. six and three-tenths _____ _____

    b. thirty-four hundredths _____ _____

    c. eleven and five hundred twenty-one thousandths _____ _____

    d. one and ninety-nine thousandths _____ _____

    e. seven and four-hundredths _____ _____

4. Change these decimals to common fractions in lowest terms.

    0.4 _____   0.25 _____   0.500 _____   0.35 _____   0.125 _____

B. *Write* <, >, *or* = *between each pair of decimals.* *(1 pt. each; 6 total)*

5. 3.0 _____ 3   6.8 _____ 6.69   4.4 _____ 4.43

6. 0.06 _____ 0.006   5.2 _____ 5.200   7.9 _____ 7.09

C. *In each set, draw a* circle *around the smallest number and a* box *around the largest number.* *(2 pt. each set; 12 total)*

7. 6.4   6.004   6.04   0.12   0.125   0.012   4.2   4.3   4.25

8. 3.18   3.8   3.81   7.056   7.065   7.5   9.5   9.15   9.52

D. *Follow the signs.* *(3 pt. each; 30 total)*

9.
$56.70
349.25
250.97
+ 39.46

$350.29
8.35
17.65
264.37
+ 25.03

$510.00
- 257.80

$4.29
× 467

$7.50
× 308

10.
655.2
- 38.45

48
- 12.169

46.78
3.375
125.1
+ 75.468

$32\overline{)\$34.56}$ $19\overline{)\$43.70}$

E. *Copy in straight columns to add or subtract. Annex zeroes to fill in empty places.* *(3 pt. each; 15 total)*

11.   12.3 + 5.67 + 418.9 + 61 = _____

12.   49.69 + 3.7 + 23.185 + 0.237 = _____

13.   420.3 − 75.48 = _____

14.   37.409 − 17.35 = _____

15.   752 − 389.99 = _____

F. *Solve these reading problems.* *(3 pt. each; 9 total)*

16. A supersonic jet flies the 3,640 miles from New York to Paris in 5 hours. How fast does the jet travel?

_____

17. A train traveling 78 miles per hour and a bus traveling 50 miles per hour are both traveling the same route. How much farther will the train travel in three hours than the bus will go in four hours? (Be careful! This is a three-step problem.)

_____

18. The Martin family traveled 4 hours to the fellowship meetings in a neighboring state. Irene and Rita recorded 46 miles traveled the first hour, 55 miles the second hour, 57 miles the third hour, and 62 miles the fourth hour. What was the average number of miles per hour that the Martins traveled?

_____

Subtract points wrong from 100% for score.

110. Chapter 11 Test

Score _____

Name _____   Date _____

A. *Write these as percents.* *(1 pt. each; 4 total)*

1. 0.35 _____   0.09 _____   0.68 _____ $\frac{97}{100}$ _____

B. *Change to hundredths and then to percents.* *(1 pt. each; 7 total)*

2. $\frac{4}{5} = \overline{}_{100} = $ _____ $\frac{1}{2} = \overline{}_{100} = $ _____ $\frac{17}{20} = \overline{}_{100} = $ _____

3. $\frac{19}{50} = $ _____ $\frac{22}{25} = $ _____ $\frac{3}{10} = $ _____ $\frac{3}{4} = $ _____

C. *Fill in the missing numbers to make equivalent fractions.* *(1 pt. each; 5 total)*

4. $\frac{2}{3} = \frac{16}{}$ $\frac{1}{} = \frac{6}{24}$ $\frac{18}{36} = \frac{}{6}$ $\frac{}{40} = \frac{4}{10}$ $\frac{3}{} = \frac{12}{16}$

D. *Write these ratios as fractions, whole numbers, or mixed numbers. All your answers should be in simplest form.* *(2 pt. each; 16 total)*

5. 15 is what part of 20? _____   8 is _____ of 40.
6. 16 compared with 36 _____   12 is what part of 48? _____
7. 13 is how many times 2? _____   the ratio of 9 to 4 _____
8. 20 is _____ times 15.   6 compared with 2 _____

E. *Use equivalent fractions to find the missing numbers.* *(2 pt. each; 18 total)*

9. $\frac{1}{4}$ yd. = _____ in. $\frac{1}{3}$ hr. = _____ min. $\frac{1}{2}$ qt. = _____ cups
10. $\frac{5}{8}$ lb. = _____ oz. $\frac{3}{4}$ yd. = _____ in. $\frac{3}{4}$ day = _____ hr.
11. $\frac{2}{3}$ ft. = _____ in. $\frac{1}{4}$ century = _____ yr. $\frac{2}{7}$ week = _____ days

F. *Tell what part the one measure is of the other. Reduce fractions.* *(2 pt. each; 18 total)*

12. 14 oz. = _____ lb.   7 eggs = _____ doz.   24 in. = _____ yd.
13. 9 mo. = _____ yr.   45 min. = _____ hr.   6 hr. = _____ day
14. 2 qt. = _____ pk.   3 qt. = _____ gal.   20 yr. = _____ century

G. *Study this bar graph, and answer the questions below it.* (2 pt. each; 12 total)

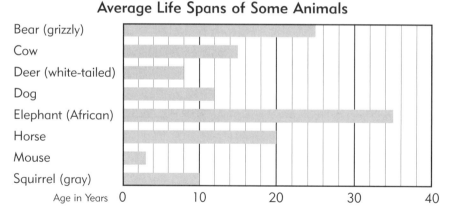

Average Life Spans of Some Animals

15. According to the graph, a squirrel usually lives _____ years longer than a white-tailed deer.

16. Which lives longer, a cow or a horse? _____ How much longer? _____

17. A dog lives _____ times as long as a mouse.

18. Write a fraction comparing how long a grizzly bear lives with how long an elephant lives. _____

19. A white-tailed deer lives only _____ as long as a horse.

H. *Solve these reading problems.* (3 pt. each; 18 total)

20. If a dozen oranges are marked $1.68, what is the price of 5 oranges?

_____

21. Father drove 180 miles on six gallons of gasoline. At that rate, how far can he go on 10 gallons of gasoline?

_____

22. In Sister Jean's fifth grade class, 63 percent of the pupils are girls. What percent of the class are boys?

_____

23. If Brother Titus drives at an average speed of 44 miles per hour, how much time should he allow for a trip of 132 miles?

_____

24. The book *Papa Leonardo* has 60 pages. If Ronald has read 100% of the book, how many pages has he read?

_____

25. Aunt Joy wants to buy 3 yards of material at $2.49 a yard. What will be her change from $10.00?

_____

Subtract points wrong from 100% for score.

123. Chapter 12 Test (Third Quarter)

Score _____

Name _____   Date _____

A. *Write the answers.* *(1: 1/2 pt. each blank; 2–8: 1 pt. each blank; 23 total)*

1. Write as decimals and as common fractions or mixed numbers.

   a. fourteen and six thousandths _____ _____

   b. seven hundredths _____ _____

   c. eighty-five and nine tenths _____ _____

2. Change these fractions to percents.

   $\frac{49}{100}$ _____ $\frac{49}{50}$ _____ $\frac{1}{2}$ _____ $\frac{3}{5}$ _____ $\frac{9}{10}$ _____

3. Fill in the missing numbers in these proportions.

   $\frac{3}{5} = \frac{}{35}$ $\frac{}{40} = \frac{7}{10}$ $\frac{3}{} = \frac{9}{36}$ $\frac{16}{48} = \frac{2}{}$

4. Write <, >, or = between each pair.

   8.099 _____ 8.10   7.00 _____ 7.0   4.65 _____ 4.6

5. What is the ratio of 3 cardinals to 6 robins? _____

6. 4 oz. = _____ lb.   8 in. = _____ ft.   30 in. = _____ yd.

7. $\frac{3}{4}$ hr. = _____ min. $\frac{1}{2}$ pk. = _____ qt. $\frac{1}{4}$ yd. = _____ in.

8. $\frac{3}{4}$ **of** a number means $\frac{3}{4}$ _____ the number.

B. *Solve these problems carefully.* *(2 pt. each; 16–18: 3 pt. each; 58 total)*

9. 231.6 + 47.75 + 28.615 = _____

10. 40 – 16.793 = _____

11.
$$\begin{array}{r} 693 \\ \times\, 604 \\ \hline \end{array} \qquad \begin{array}{r} \$24.07 \\ \times\quad 57 \\ \hline \end{array} \qquad \begin{array}{r} 13\frac{2}{3} \\ \times\, 9 \\ \hline \end{array} \qquad \begin{array}{r} 16 \\ \times\, 5\frac{3}{4} \\ \hline \end{array}$$

12.
$$\begin{array}{r} \$38.02 \\ 624.85 \\ 147.36 \\ +\ 50.44 \\ \hline \end{array} \qquad 27\overline{)23{,}121} \qquad 83\overline{)\$504.64}$$

13. $\$603.05$ $\frac{2}{3}$ $\frac{9}{10}$ 14 $11\frac{5}{8}$
        $-\ 275.94$ $\frac{1}{6}$ $\frac{4}{5}$ $-\ 6\frac{5}{12}$ $-\ 4\frac{1}{3}$
                        $+\ \frac{4}{9}$ $+\ \frac{1}{2}$

14. $\frac{3}{4} \times 10 =$ $4 \times \frac{5}{8} =$ $\frac{7}{16} \times \frac{4}{5} =$

15. $18 \times \frac{2}{9} =$ $\frac{1}{3} \times 7 =$ $\frac{3}{4} \times \frac{8}{9} =$

16. $9 \div \frac{1}{3} =$ $\frac{3}{5} \div 6 =$

17. $\frac{2}{3} \div \frac{4}{5} =$ $\frac{7}{8} \div \frac{1}{2} =$

18. $\frac{1}{5} \div \frac{9}{10} =$ $7 \div \frac{7}{16} =$

C. *Solve these reading problems.* *(3 pt. each; 24 total)*

19. In the United States, 22% of the people are 14 years old or younger. What percent of the people are older than 14?

_____

20. Beverly has only 2 cups of milk. How many batches of cookies can she make if each batch takes $\frac{2}{3}$ cup?

_____

21. Kathy's recipe for brownies calls for 2 cups of chocolate chips. Mother told Kathy to use only $\frac{3}{4}$ of the chocolate chips called for in the recipe. How many cups should Kathy use?

_____

22. A 13-ounce box of cereal is priced $1.82. What is the price per ounce?

_____

23. How many yards are in 9,000 inches?

_____

24. Vegetables are marked 3 cans for $1.19. What is the price of 12 cans?

_____

25. If 5 apples cost 80¢, what is the cost of 3 apples?

_____

26. At 45 miles per hour, how far can a car travel in 3 hours?

_____

Subtract points wrong from 100% for score.

132. Chapter 13 Test

Score _____

Name _____ Date _____

A. *Write the correct letter to match each description. You will not use all the letters.* *(2 pt. each; 14 total)*

a. gram

b. liter

____ **1.** The basic metric unit of length.

c. meter

____ **2.** The basic metric unit of weight.

d. centimeter

____ **3.** A unit that is a little more than a quart.

e. millimeter

____ **4.** A unit that is a little less than $\frac{1}{2}$ inch.

f. furlong

____ **5.** A unit that is equal to about 18 inches.

g. fathom

h. cubit

____ **6.** A unit that is equal to $\frac{1}{9}$ mile.

i. Celsius

____ **7.** The most common scale for measuring temperature in the United States.

j. Fahrenheit

B. *Fill in the blanks with numbers from the box. You may write some numbers more than once and some not at all.* *(2 pt. each; 16 total)*

8. A kilogram is equal to _____ grams.   10

9. A meter is equal to _____ centimeters.   100

10. A centimeter is equal to _____ millimeters.   1,000

11. A kilometer is equal to _____ meters.   39

12. A liter equals _____ milliliters.

13. A gram is about _____ ounce.   0.035

14. A kilogram is about _____ pounds. $\frac{1}{5}$

15. A meter is about _____ inches.   2.2

C. *Follow the directions.* *(16: 1 pt. each; 17–18: 2 pt. each; 20 total)*

16. Write the meaning of each metric prefix.

   a. deka- _____   **c.** centi- _____   **e.** hecto- _____

   b. milli- _____   **d.** kilo- _____   **f.** deci- _____

17. Underline the most sensible answers.

   a. A fifth grader might weigh 38 (grams, milligrams, kilograms).

   b. This paper is about 20 (millimeters, centimeters, meters) wide.

   c. A calcium tablet might contain 200 (grams, milligrams, kilograms) of calcium.

   d. A schoolroom may be 10 (meters, centimeters, kilometers) long.

   e. A Thermos jug holds about 4 (liters, milliliters) of juice.

18. Write the temperatures shown on these thermometers.

a. _____   b. _____

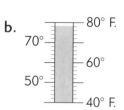

D. *Write the correct numbers in the blanks.* (2 pt. each item; 20 total)

19. 3 meters = _____ millimeters   14 meters = _____ centimeters

20. 7,000 meters = _____ kilometers   7,000 meters = _____ dekameters

21. 25 centimeters = _____ millimeters   14 liters = _____ milliliters

22. 110 millimeters = _____ centimeters   2 kilograms = _____ grams

23. 75 mm = ____ cm ____ mm = ____ cm   38 mm = ____ cm ____ mm = ____ cm

E. *Write the lengths (in centimeters) indicated on this metric ruler.* (2 pt. each item; 10 total)

24. a. _____   b. _____   c. _____   d. _____   e. _____

a. ↓   b. ↓   c. ↓   d. ↓   e. ↓

0   1cm   2   3   4   5   6   7   8   9   10   11   12   13

F. *Solve these problems.* (3 pt. each; 21 total)

25.   15 feet 7 inches   7 pounds   8 ounces   4 gallons 2 quarts
     + 6 feet 8 inches   − 5 pounds 12 ounces   × 4

26. Mrs. Monroe bought a 40-kilogram bag of sugar. She used 1.75 kilograms to make jelly. How many kilograms were left?

_____

27. The temple Solomon built for God was 60 cubits long and 20 cubits wide. In English units, the temple was _____ feet long and _____ feet wide.

28. At the wedding that Jesus attended in Cana were six stone waterpots that could hold about 66 liters apiece. Jesus told the servants to fill the waterpots with water. How many liters did the six waterpots hold?

_____

29. One month's income at Florin's Dry Goods was $5,176.30. Expenses were $1,835.48 for the goods sold, $1,450.00 for wages, and $729.75 for other costs. What was the profit that month?

_____

Subtract points wrong from 100% for score.

141. Chapter 14 Test

Score _____

Name _____ Date _____

A. *Write as decimals and as common fractions or mixed numbers.* *(1 pt. each blank; 6 total)*

1. forty-seven hundredths _____ _____

2. eighteen and three tenths _____ _____

3. six and twenty-five thousandths _____ _____

B. *Circle the smallest number in each set.* *(2 pt. each set; 12 total)*

4. 1.03   1.3   1.003   0.06   0.16   0.61

5. 0.8   0.9   0.10   4.5   4.12   4.099

6. 0.2   0.17   0.25   6.017   6.07   6.17

C. *Fill in the blanks.* *(2 pt. each blank; 20 total)*

7. On the Fahrenheit temperature scale, the freezing point is _____° and the boiling point is _____°.

8. On the Celsius scale, the freezing point is _____° and the boiling point is _____°.

9. A meter equals _____ centimeters.

10. A centimeter is equal to _____ millimeters.

11. A kilometer is equal to _____ meters.

12. A _____ is a metric measure a little larger than a quart.

13. A _____ is a metric measure of about 0.035 ounce.

14. A _____ is equal to 1,000 grams.

D. *What pieces of money should be given as change?* *(3 pt. each; 6 total)*

15. Amount of purchase—$6.57;   amount given—$10.00

_____

16. Amount of purchase—$8.30;   amount given—$20.00

_____

E. *Find the answers.* *(2 pt. each; 44 total)*

17.
$3.78	$45.09	$5.60	6.7	0.485
× 6	× 27	× 425	× 3	× 8

18.   0.45   38.4   97   813   208
          × 18   × 74   × 4.6   × 5.07   × 0.179

19. 8)$132.00   6)$764.52   27)$36.72   43)$46.44

20.   8)0.056   5)0.75   3)0.117   9)1.26

21. 12)318.0   19)6.65   36)0.936   24)326.4

F. *Solve these reading problems.* *(3 pt. each; 12 total)*

22. Boys' socks are marked 3 pairs for $3.95. What is the price for 6 pairs of socks?

_____

23. The price of 36 verse stickers is $1.08. What is the price of one sticker?

_____

24. A year's subscription to *The Christian Pathway* in 1994 was $6.50 for one copy and $27.50 for five copies. How much was saved per copy by buying five copies?

_____

25. Sylvia's brother keeps a record of the gasoline he puts into his car. One time he drove 785.0 miles on 25 gallons of gasoline. How many miles per gallon did he drive?

_____

Subtract points wrong from 100% for score.

151. Chapter 15 Test

Score _____

Name _____   Date _____

A. *Name the geometric symbols and shapes shown below. Choose words from the box.* (2 pt. each; 24 total)

1. ☐   _____

2. ←→   _____

3. ⌐   _____

4. ⋈   _____

5. ⬡   _____

6. ═   _____

7. ⯃   _____

8. ▷   _____

9. ⊥   _____

10. ▱   _____

11. ·   _____

12. ⊖   _____

parallel lines
perpendicular lines
intersecting lines
right angle
acute angle
obtuse angle
line segment
line
point
square
rectangle
triangle
pentagon
octagon
hexagon
parallelogram
radius
diameter

B. *Find the answers.* (2 pt. each; 20 total)

13. Find the perimeters of these shapes.

a. _____   b. _____   c. _____   d. _____

21" 18.3"
29.5"

$8\frac{1}{2}'$
$5\frac{1}{2}'$ $5\frac{1}{2}'$
$8\frac{1}{2}'$

8.2 ft.
8.2 ft.

17 yd.
11 yd.

14. Find the areas of these squares and rectangles.

a. _____   b. _____   c. _____   d. _____

11 cm
11 cm

32"
14"

7"
7"

8.5'
5'

15. Find the areas of rectangles with these dimensions.

a. length—$13\frac{1}{2}$ feet   width—8 feet _____

b. length—17 inches   width—9.3 inches _____

C. *Write* true *or* false. (1 pt. each; 8 total)

16. _____ Figures with the same size and shape are called similar figures.

17. _____ Parallelograms have four right angles.

18. _____ Intersecting lines cross each other.

19. _____ The hands of a clock at 7:00 form an obtuse angle.

20. _____ A hexagon has eight sides.

21. _____ To find the area of a rectangle, you should multiply the length and the width.

22. _____ Perimeter is the distance around a figure.

23. _____ An acre is much smaller than a square mile.

D. *Fill in the blanks.* (1 pt. each; 4 total)

24. 1 square yard = _____ square feet   45 sq. ft. = _____ sq. yd.

25. 1 square foot = _____ square inches   45 sq. yd. = _____ sq. ft.

E. *Do the work mentally, and write only the answers.* *(2 pt. each; 32 total)*

26.   19 + 25 = _____   18 + 16 = _____   35 + 15 = _____   19 + 17 = _____

27.   31 – 7 = _____   40 – 6 = _____   24 – 7 = _____   35 – 8 = _____

28.   30 – 16 = _____   28 – 12 = _____   32 – 17 = _____   23 – 14 = _____

29.   5 × 15 = _____   7 × 13 = _____   4 × 27 = _____   6 × 24 = _____

F. *Solve these reading problems.* *(3 pt. each; 12 total)*

30.   (Draw a sketch for this one.)
      The dimensions of the Bylers' living room are 14 feet by 18
      feet. What is the perimeter of the room?

      _____

31.   Find how many square feet of carpet it takes to cover the floor
      of this living room (see number 30).

      _____

32.   The property of the Jonestown Christian Day School measures
      125 yards long and 80 yards wide. What is its area?

      _____

33.   There are 43,560 square feet in an acre. How many square
      yards is that? (Think: How many square feet are in a square
      yard?)

      _____

161. Chapter 16 Test

Score _____

Name _____ Date _____

A. *Follow the directions.* (2 pt. each; 22 total)

1. Write =, <, or > in each blank.

6.25 _____ 6.4   0.370 _____ 0.37   4.1 _____ 4.17

2. Write numerals for these number words.

   a. eighteen million, sixty-three _____

   b. seven hundred fifty-two billion _____

3. Round 62,495 to the nearest hundred. _____

4. Round 62,495 to the nearest thousand. _____

5. Round 3,872,169 to the nearest hundred thousand. _____

6. Write the missing numbers.

9 yd. = _____ ft.   9 ft. = _____ yd.   9 in. = _____ ft.

B. *Do these exercises.* (3 pt. each; 30 total)

7. Find the perimeters.

   a. _____   **b.** _____

   a. 13 ft. / 13 ft. (square)
   b. 23 cm / 15 cm (rectangle)

8. Find the areas of the two shapes in number 7. Use proper labels!

   a. _____   **b.** _____

9. Find the actual distances represented by these lines on the scale drawings below.

    a. Line EF _____

    b. Line FG _____

    c. Line JK _____

    d. Line JM _____

    e. Line ST _____

    f. Line TU _____

Scale: $\frac{1}{2}$ " = 1 ft.

Scale: $\frac{1}{8}$ " = 1'

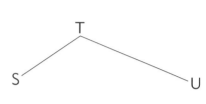

Scale: 1 in. = 12 mi.

C. *This line graph shows Arnold's spelling grades for twelve lessons. Use the graph to answer the questions below.* (4 pt. each; 16 total)

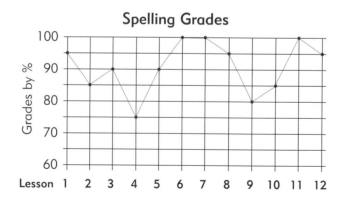

10. What grade did Arnold have on Lesson 8? _____

11. On how many of the 12 lessons did Arnold receive 100%? _____

12. What was Arnold's lowest spelling grade? _____

13. How much did Arnold's spelling grade rise from Lesson 4 to Lesson 5? _____

D. *Use the map of Guatemala to do these exercises. Cities are marked by dots.* (4 pt. each; 8 total)

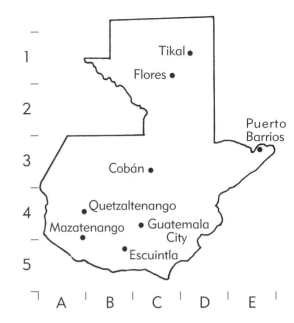

14. The capital of Guatemala is located at C4. Write the name.

_____

15. Before white men came to Guatemala, the Maya Indians controlled this area. Ruins of large Indian temples can still be seen near the city located at D1. Write its name.

_____

E. *Solve these reading problems. Do the work on other paper.* (4 pt. each; 20 total)

16. If a map has a scale of 1 inch = 300 miles, what distance is represented by a $2\frac{1}{2}$-inch line?

_____

17. A drawing has a scale of $\frac{1}{4}$ inch = 1 foot. How much does $\frac{1}{8}$ inch on the drawing represent?

_____

18. A piece of plywood measures 4 feet by 8 feet. How large an area can be covered by 12 sheets of plywood?

_____

19. Manasseh reigned as king of Judah for 55 years. His son Amon reigned only 2 years. Manasseh's reign was how many times as long as Amon's reign?

_____

20. At Jones' Farm Market, Mr. Howard bought $2\frac{1}{2}$ pounds of spinach at $0.98 a pound and 2 bunches of radishes at 59¢ a bunch. What was his total bill?

_____

Subtract points wrong from 100% for score.

170. Chapter 17 Test (Final)

Score _____

Name _____ Date _____

A. Write the answers only. *(1/2 pt. each; 15 1/2 total)*

1. $\begin{array}{r} 12 \\ \times\ 11 \\ \hline \end{array}$ $\begin{array}{r} 8 \\ \times\ 9 \\ \hline \end{array}$ $\begin{array}{r} 11 \\ \times\ 11 \\ \hline \end{array}$ $\begin{array}{r} 12 \\ \times\ 9 \\ \hline \end{array}$ $\begin{array}{r} 7 \\ \times\ 8 \\ \hline \end{array}$ $\begin{array}{r} 10 \\ \times\ 12 \\ \hline \end{array}$ $\begin{array}{r} 12 \\ \times\ 7 \\ \hline \end{array}$ $\begin{array}{r} 6 \\ \times\ 8 \\ \hline \end{array}$ $\begin{array}{r} 4 \\ \times\ 9 \\ \hline \end{array}$

2. $8\overline{)64}$ $11\overline{)110}$ $12\overline{)60}$ $10\overline{)120}$ $9\overline{)54}$ $7\overline{)63}$

3. 31 + 27 = _____   26 + 17 = _____   16 + 14 = _____   35 + 20 = _____

4. 27 – 9 = _____   29 – 13 = _____   31 – 5 = _____   33 – 18 = _____

5. 10 × 354 = _____   100 × 40 = _____   4 × 17 = _____   3 × 28 = _____

6. $\frac{2}{3}$ of 18 = _____ $\frac{4}{5}$ of 30 = _____ $1\frac{1}{2}$ × 16 = _____ $3\frac{1}{4}$ × 12 = _____

B. Follow the directions. *(1/2 pt. each; 19 1/2 total)*

7. Write numerals for these number words.
    a. three hundred fifty billion _____
    b. seven billion, one hundred million, thirty-five _____
    c. forty-nine and eight hundredths _____

8. What is the value of the 3 in 45,369,028,157? _____

9. Write the number that means 40,000 + 5,000 + 200 + 90 + 7. _____

10. Write as Arabic numerals: MCDLXXXVII _____   MMDCCXLIX _____

11. Change to decimals: $3\frac{27}{100}$ _____ $14\frac{6}{1,000}$ _____

12. Change to percents: $\frac{27}{100}$ _____ $\frac{17}{20}$ _____ $\frac{3}{4}$ _____ $\frac{9}{10}$ _____

13. Round 356,824 to the nearest thousand. _____

14. Round $45.39 to the nearest dollar. _____

15. Write the measurements to which the arrows point.

    a. _____ b. _____ c. _____ d. _____ e. _____ f. _____

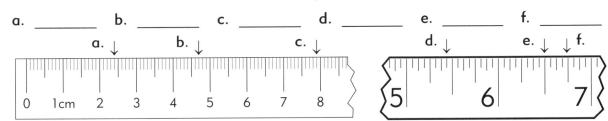

16. Write four multiples of 12. _____

17. Write four factors of 12. _____

18. Write <, >, or = between each pair.

   a. 0.061 _____ 0.42   3.17 _____ 3.170   4.5 _____ 4.05

   b. $\frac{5}{8}$ _____ $\frac{1}{2}$ $\frac{9}{16}$ _____ $\frac{3}{4}$ $\frac{2}{3}$ _____ $\frac{3}{5}$ $\frac{5}{6}$ _____ $\frac{3}{4}$

19. Write in simplest form: $\frac{16}{28}$ _____ $\frac{15}{40}$ _____ $\frac{24}{48}$ _____ $\frac{5}{2}$ _____

20. What fraction means 3 divided by 8? _____

21. Write **yes** or **no**.

   Is 3,732 divisible by 3? _____   by 4? _____   by 6? _____   by 9? _____

C. *Write the numbers that belong in the blanks.* *(1/2 pt. each; 9 total)*

22. 1 yard = _____ inches   1 bushel = _____ pecks   1 ton = _____ pounds

23. 1 quart = _____ pints   1 century = _____ years   1 year = _____ weeks

24. 1 mile = _____ feet   1 leap year = _____ days

25. 1 kilometer = _____ meters   1 centimeter = _____ millimeters

26. 1 square yard = _____ square feet   1 square foot = _____ square inches

27. 4 gal. = _____ qt.   2 hr. = _____ min.   6 ft. = _____ yd.

28. 3 yr. = _____ mo.   18 in. = _____ ft.   30 min. = _____ hr.

D. *Fill in the blanks.* *(1 pt. each blank; 2 pt. for all of number 42; 16 total)*

29. The _____ is the basic metric unit of length.

30. The _____ is a Bible measure equal to about $1\frac{1}{2}$ feet.

31. The _____ is a metric measure about equal to a quart.

32. The answer to a multiplication problem is the _____ .

33. _____ is measured with square units.

34. The _____ is the basic metric unit of weight, equal to about 0.035 of an ounce.

35. The top number of a fraction is the _____ .

36. To find how many more, you _____ .

37. To find $\frac{2}{3}$ of a number, you _____ by $\frac{2}{3}$.

38. An octagon has _____ sides.

39. The angle formed by clock hands at 9:00 has the name _____ angle.

40. The prefix **kilo-** means _____ .

41. a. The perimeter of the rectangle at the right is _____ .

b. The area of the rectangle at the right is _____ .

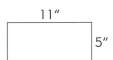

42. Amount of purchase—$6.29; amount given—$20.00

Coins and bills that should be given as change:

_____ _____ _____ _____ _____

E. *Copy in straight columns and solve.* (*1 pt. each; 4 total*)

43. $56.7 + 3.92 + 476.25 + 3.384 =$ _____

44. $\$8 + \$43.59 + \$5.95 + \$125 =$ _____

45. $700.4 - 25.76 =$ _____

46. $\$580 - \$329.06 =$ _____

F. *Work carefully.* (*1 pt. each; 22 total*)

47.
$$\begin{array}{r} 13 \text{ min.} \quad 45 \text{ sec.} \\ + 25 \text{ min.} \quad 35 \text{ sec.} \\ \hline \end{array}$$
$$\begin{array}{r} 15 \text{ feet} \quad 6 \text{ inches} \\ - 7 \text{ feet} \quad 10 \text{ inches} \\ \hline \end{array}$$
$$\begin{array}{r} 5 \text{ qt.} \quad 2 \text{ cups} \\ \times 5 \\ \hline \end{array}$$

48.
$$\begin{array}{r} 27{,}356 \\ 15{,}690 \\ 42{,}689 \\ + 36{,}145 \\ \hline \end{array}$$
$$\begin{array}{r} 82{,}601 \\ - 24{,}574 \\ \hline \end{array}$$
$$\begin{array}{r} 650 \\ \times 67 \\ \hline \end{array}$$
$$\begin{array}{r} 408 \\ \times 764 \\ \hline \end{array}$$
$$\begin{array}{r} 39.2 \\ \times 85 \\ \hline \end{array}$$

49. $8\overline{)9{,}456}$ $\qquad$ $17\overline{)5{,}202}$ $\qquad$ $43\overline{)64{,}617}$ $\qquad$ $7\overline{)0.56}$ $\qquad$ $26\overline{)93.6}$

50.
$$\begin{array}{r} \frac{7}{8} \\ \frac{3}{4} \\ + \frac{1}{2} \\ \hline \end{array}$$
$$\begin{array}{r} 7\frac{1}{2} \\ + 5\frac{5}{6} \\ \hline \end{array}$$
$$\begin{array}{r} 8\frac{3}{8} \\ - 2\frac{5}{8} \\ \hline \end{array}$$
$$\begin{array}{r} 10 \\ - 6\frac{7}{12} \\ \hline \end{array}$$
$$\begin{array}{r} 6\frac{1}{3} \\ - 1\frac{3}{4} \\ \hline \end{array}$$

51. $\frac{3}{4} \times \frac{4}{5} =$ $\qquad$ $\frac{7}{8} \times 4 =$ $\qquad$ $\frac{11}{12} \div \frac{1}{4} =$ $\qquad$ $\frac{3}{5} \div 3 =$

G. *Solve these reading problems.* (2 pt. each; 14 total)

52. The sewing circle of the Elkville Mennonite Church is making dresses for use in Guatemala and Paraguay. A small girl's dress takes $\frac{3}{4}$ yard of material. How many small dresses can be cut from a 6-yard piece of material?

_____

53. The scale of miles on a map is 1 inch = 500 miles. What is the actual distance between two cities that are $1\frac{1}{2}$ inches apart on the map?

_____

54. The scale on a drawing is $\frac{1}{4}$ inch = 1 foot. What actual length is represented by $1\frac{1}{4}$ inch on the drawing?

_____

55. The spruce tree is a common evergreen that usually grows to a height of about 40 feet. The giant redwood tree grows 300 feet tall. A 300-foot redwood is how many times as tall as a 40-foot spruce tree?

_____

56. Pennsylvania usually receives about 40 inches of rain per year. One month during a dry year, some parts of Pennsylvania received only 0.3 inch. At that rate, how many inches of rain would fall in a year?

_____

57. Father traveled to Florida for a week of revival meetings. The odometer of the car showed 56,729 miles when he left home and 59,457 miles when he returned. How many miles had Father driven since he left home?

_____

58. At a rate of 55 miles per hour, how far will a car travel in 5 hours?

_____